Garfield
A Gift For You

JiM DAViS

ℛ
RAVETTE PUBLISHING

First published by
Ravette Books Limited 1992
Reprinted 1992, 1993 (twice)
Reprinted by Ravette Publishing Limited
1996 (twice), 1997

Printed and bound in Great Britain
for Ravette Publishing Limited,
Unit 3, Tristar Centre,
Star Road, Partridge Green,
West Sussex RH13 8RA
by Cox & Wyman Ltd, Reading, Berkshire

ISBN 1 85304 190 4

© 1991 United Feature Syndicate, Inc.

© 1991 United Feature Syndicate, Inc.

© 1991 United Feature Syndicate, inc.

JIM DAVIS 1-24

© 1991 United Feature Syndicate, Inc.

© 1991 United Feature Syndicate, Inc.

© 1991 United Feature Syndicate, Inc.

© 1991 United Feature Syndicate, Inc.

© 1991 United Feature Syndicate, Inc.

THE MAILMAN ALREADY CAME TODAY, GARFIELD

HE DID?

© 1991 United Feature Syndicate, Inc.

© 1991 United Feature Syndicate, Inc.

© 1991 United Feature Syndicate, Inc.

WAH-HA! HA! HA!

BOY, HAIRCUTS ARE DECEIVING

JIM DAVIS 4-2

© 1991 United Feature Syndicate, Inc.

© 1991 United Feature Syndicate, Inc.

© 1991 United Feature Syndicate, Inc.

JIM DAVIS 4-15

UH... GARFIELD...

BECAUSE NAP ATTACKS CAN STRIKE ANYTIME, ANYWHERE, WITHOUT WARNING, THAT'S WHY

JIM DAVIS 4-16

© 1991 United Feature Syndicate, Inc.

© 1991 United Feature Syndicate, Inc.

© 1991 United Feature Syndicate, Inc.

© 1991 United Feature Syndicate, Inc.

© 1991 United Feature Syndicate, Inc.

© 1991 United Feature Syndicate, Inc.

© 1991 United Feature Syndicate, Inc.

NOW THAT WE'RE DONE READING OUR NEWSPAPER, MAYBE WE CAN SCRATCH OUR TUMMY

JIM DAVIS 5-9

© 1991 United Feature Syndicate, Inc.

JIM DAVIS 5-20

GOOSH!

© 1991 United Feature Syndicate, Inc.

FROM NOW ON, LET'S BE PUTTING WATER IN THE WATER DISH, AND FOOD IN THE FOOD DISH, OKAY?

SOME PEOPLE HAVE EXCITING LIVES

SOME SEEK ADVENTURE AND ROMANCE

© 1991 United Feature Syndicate, Inc.

AND SOME STAY HOME AND TEASE THEIR EYEBROWS

GARFIELD I NEED A HOBBY

JIM DAVIS 5-27

JIM DAVIS 5-31

OTHER GARFIELD BOOKS IN THIS SERIES

COLOUR TV SPECIALS

A Garfield Christmas	£3.99
Garfield's Thanksgiving	£2.95

GARFIELD THEME BOOKS

Garfield's Guide to Behaving Badly	£3.99
Garfield's Guide to Insults	£3.99
Garfield's Guide to Pigging Out	£3.99
Garfield's Guide to Romance	£3.99

All Ravette books are available at your local bookshop or from the address below. Just tick the titles required and send the form with your remittance to:-

B.B.C.S., P.O. BOX 941, HULL, NORTH HUMBERSIDE HU1 3YQ
24 Hour Telephone Credit Card Line 01482 224626
Prices and availability are subject to change without notice.

Please enclose a cheque or postal order made payable to B.B.C.S. to the value of the cover price of the book and allow the following for postage and packing:

U.K. & B.F.P.O:	£1.00 for the first book and 50p for each additional book to a maximum of £3.50.
Overseas & Eire	£2.00 for the first book, £1.00 for the second and 50p for each additional book.

BLOCK CAPITALS PLEASE

Name ....

Address...

....

....

Cards accepted: Mastercard and Visa

☐☐☐☐☐☐☐☐☐☐☐☐☐☐☐☐☐☐

Expiry Date .... Signature ....